Robert watched as lighted matches were applied to the breaches of the guns. Seconds later flames spouted from their muzzles. A great roar echoed across the water and the pirate ship disappeared behind a cloud of smoke. Cannon-balls whistled over the junk, falling harmlessly into the water beyond.

Robert brandished his shotgun in the air like a spear. 'Cowards!' he screamed. 'Miserable scum!'

The pirates responded with a second broadside. This time the shots fell closer, one narrowly missing the main mast. At that moment a horrible thought flashed through Robert's tangled mind. His samples! If he were killed, all the seeds and plants he had brought on board would be lost. They were of no use to anyone else, least of all pirates. Furthermore, if he did not return to Shanghai to pay the warehouse, his collection there would probably be tipped into the harbour. Years of painstaking work would be wasted!

Also by Eden Project Books:

REVENGE OF THE GREEN PLANET
Astounding Facts About Plants

STEWART ROSS

Pirates, Plants and Plunder!

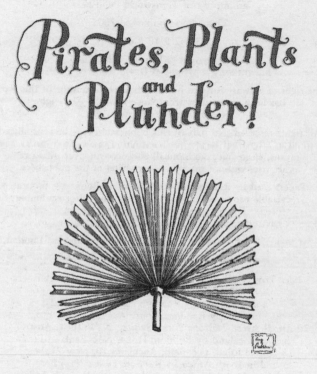

Illustrated by David Roberts

Eden Project Books

PIRATES, PLANTS AND PLUNDER!
AN EDEN PROJECT BOOK 1 903 91935 5

Published in Great Britain by Eden Project Books,
an imprint of Transworld Publishers

This edition published 2005

1 3 5 7 9 10 8 6 4 2

Set in 11.5/17pt Sabon by Palimpsest Book Production Limited,
Polmont, Stirlingshire

Eden Project Books are published by Transworld Publishers
61–63 Uxbridge Road, London W5 5SA,
a division of The Random House Group Ltd,
in Australia by Random House Australia (Pty) Ltd,
20 Alfred Street, Milsons Point, Sydney, NSW 2061, Australia,
in New Zealand by Random House New Zealand Ltd,
18 Poland Road, Glenfield, Auckland 10, New Zealand,
and in South Africa by Random House (Pty) Ltd,
Endulini, 5A Jubilee Road, Parktown 2193, South Africa

THE RANDOM HOUSE GROUP Limited Reg. No. 954009
www.kidsatrandomhouse.co.uk

www.edenproject.com

A CIP catalogue record for this book is available from the British Library.

Printed and bound in Great Britain by
Cox & Wyman Ltd., Reading, Berkshire

Pirates, Plants and Plunder!

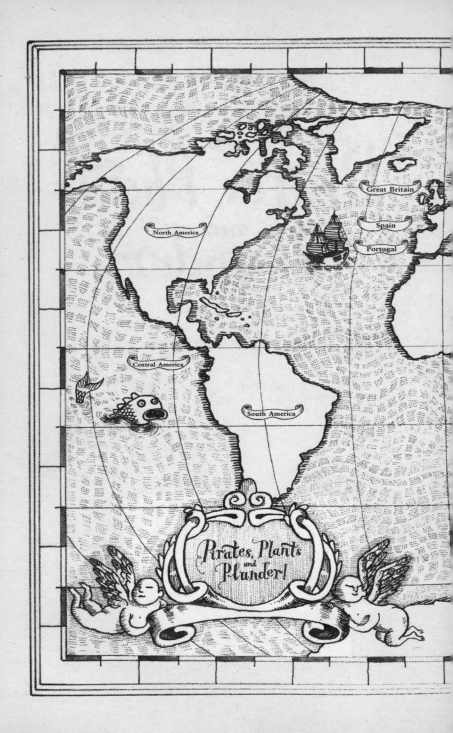

North America

Central America

South America

Great Britain

Spain

Portugal

Pirates, Plants
and
Plunder!

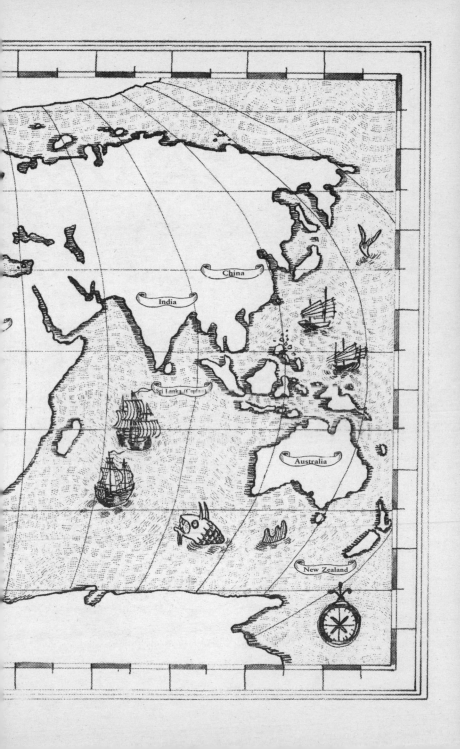

CONTENTS

Robert Fortune

*I*n the mid-nineteenth century, the Scotsman
Robert Fortune (1812–1880) went to China
several times to search for rare plants. As well as
introducing many exotic and beautiful species to the
West, he also collected the seedlings that established
the world-famous tea industries of India and Ceylon
(now Sri Lanka), where lots of the tea we drink
today is grown. As China was then a troubled and
lawless land, before setting out he asked his tightfisted
employers to provide him with arms . . .

'Guns, Mr Fortune?' The chairman of the Horticultural Society stared at Robert over the top of his half-moon glasses.

The young botanist was close to despair. I could more easily get sap out of a fossil, he thought, than an extra sixpence out of this lot.

'We are a peaceful organization,' the chairman went on, scowling round the committee like an ancient walrus. 'We are dedicated to natural beauty and have no interest in firearms.'

'Not even for self-defence, Sir Horace?'

The chairman's eyebrows shot upward. 'Self-defence? You'll carry a walking stick, won't you?'

Robert took a deep breath. He'd have one more go, and if it didn't work he'd go home to Scotland.

'What could I do with a walking stick, Sir Horace, if I were surrounded by a howling mob?'

A warm glow began to spread across the walrus's face. 'For a start, Fortune, it will show that you are an English gentleman—'

'I'm a Scot, Sir Horace.'

'Well, a Scottish gentleman then.'

'And?'

The glow deepened. 'And the mob will respect

you and, if they have any decency, go home.'
Mopping his brow with a large blue handkerchief,
Sir Horace looked around his committee for support.

Although there were one or two nods, the majority
stared awkwardly at their fingers.

That's it, thought Robert. He was longing to
search China for the samples the Society wanted,
but he refused to go unless they equipped him
properly. What would be the point in collecting
every flower in China if bandits skewered him to a
tree before he could bring them home?

'Sir Horace,' he began, 'either you provide me
with a gun, or—'

'Excuse me, Mr Chairman,' interrupted a young
gentleman in a mustard-coloured waistcoat, 'but may
I say a word?'

'Of course, Lord Tankerton.'

'My uncle, Admiral Charlie Foster, has served in
the China region. He told me some pretty horrible
things about the place, too – thugs chopping chaps
up and that sort of thing. Wouldn't do our reputation
much good if poor old Fortune ended up in little
bits because we wouldn't give him a gun, would it?'

Sir Horace sighed and wiped his glasses on his
handkerchief. 'Well, gentlemen, perhaps Lord

Tankerton's remarks do throw a new light on the matter . . . ?'

The new light did the trick. Fifteen minutes later Robert Fortune had accepted the Horticultural Society's offer to search for a variety of China's exotic plants, shrubs and trees. In return they would pay him one hundred pounds a year and arm him with a shotgun and two pistols.

As Robert was leaving the building, Lord Tankerton called after him. 'Just thought I'd wish you luck, Fortune!' he said, grasping him by the hand.

'Thank you, my lord. And thank you for supporting me over the guns. Mind you, I hope I won't need them.'

Tankerton laughed. 'Need them? Oh, you'll need them, Fortune. Bet you a fiver you will.'

Robert spent almost three years in China. During this period he built up a remarkable collection of seeds and small plants, including tree peonies, cypresses, cedars and anemones that were unknown outside the Far East. He learned enough of the language to speak with the local people. After he had got used to their customs, he found the Chinese helpful and kindly. Most of them, anyway.

The mighty Chinese Empire was at that time in decline. Law and order was not upheld as it had once been, and on occasion Robert found himself in some danger. He was robbed, jostled by crowds, chased by a mob, and almost fell into a deep pit lined with bamboo spikes. But on none of these occasions did he need his guns. Nor were they required when he feared for his life in a storm at sea. In short, after more than two years in China, Robert began to think that Sir Horace had been right all along. A stout stick had been quite sufficient for personal protection.

'Ah well,' Robert chuckled to himself, 'at least I'll win the fiver from Lord Tankerton!'

By the autumn of 1845 Robert's time in the Far East was almost at an end. He had just finished a tour round northern China. To reach Shanghai, where most of his plant collection was in a warehouse waiting to be shipped back to Britain, he took a berth on a junk, a Chinese ship sailing down the coast from Ningpo.

Just before the vessel left, Robert was struck down by a violent fever. Hardly knowing where he was or what he was doing, he staggered on board and collapsed into his bunk below deck.

For three days, as the junk sailed slowly south, Robert lay delirious and sweating on his flea-ridden bed. At around noon on the fourth day he was roused to semi-consciousness by anxious shouts from the crew. He tried to concentrate on what they were saying. 'Jan-dous! Jan-dous!' He had heard the word before but was too confused to remember what it meant.

Then it came to him. 'Jan-dous' was a pirate ship! Without thinking, Robert took his pistols and shotgun from their cases and lurched like a drunken man onto the deck. The captain took one look at him and ordered him back to his cabin. 'Too dangerous here for you, Mr Fortune,' he explained.

Wearing only his sweat-soaked yellow nightshirt, Robert leaned against the mast and stared zombie-like about him. If he had heard the captain's order, it had made no impression on his fever-stricken brain. The captain shrugged and turned away. He had more important things to attend to than a mad foreigner who wanted to get himself killed.

Robert raised his bloodshot eyes. On the port side five pirate vessels were closing fast. Their decks were crowded with men armed to the teeth with every kind of blood-curdling weapon. More alarming still, the crew of the nearest ship could clearly be seen loading four ancient brass cannon.

Only half understanding what he was looking at, Robert watched as lighted matches were applied to the breaches of the guns. Seconds later flames spouted from their muzzles. A great roar echoed across the water and the pirate ship disappeared behind a cloud of smoke. Cannon-balls whistled over the junk, falling harmlessly into the water beyond.

Robert brandished his shotgun in the air like a spear. 'Cowards!' he screamed. 'Miserable scum!'

The pirates responded with a second broadside. This time the shots fell closer, one narrowly missing the main mast. At that moment a horrible thought flashed through Robert's tangled mind. His samples! If he were killed, all the seeds and plants he had brought on board would be lost. They were of no use to anyone else, least of all pirates. Furthermore, if he did not return to Shanghai to pay the warehouse, his collection there would probably be tipped into the harbour. Years of painstaking work would be wasted.

Fear of failure, combined with delirium, produced in Robert a sort of insane courage. 'Stay at your posts!' he cried to the helmsmen. 'If you don't, well, it'll be the worse for you!' Quite what he meant, he had no idea. The threat worked, however, and the doughty sailors remained at the ship's wheel.

The first pirate ship was now barely twenty metres away. Robert could see the pirates' laughing faces quite clearly. Obscene taunts flew towards him like poisonous arrows over the narrowing sea. He became even angrier.

'You villains! You'll never take us!' he shouted.

Just then he heard the voice of the captain somewhere to his left. 'Please get down, Mr Fortune! Get down, sir!'

His tone was so urgent that Robert flopped to the deck. Half a second later a cannon-ball whizzed through the space where he had been standing.

'Good lord!' he gasped. 'I could have been on the end of that! This won't do, you know.' Using his shotgun as a stick, he clambered to his feet.

The pirates were now only three or four metres away. 'Get back, you rats!' screamed Robert, pointing his gun at the thronging deck opposite. Jeers and hoots were the only reply.

Robert fired both barrels at almost point-blank range. The effect was remarkable. Several men fell to the deck, dead or wounded. The other pirates, amazed to meet with such fierce resistance, totally lost their composure. Fearing another blast of shot, they flung themselves to the deck or scampered down into the hold. Without a helmsman to keep it steady, the ship's wheel spun aimlessly. The vessel lurched to one side, out of control, its sails flapping like injured birds. Within a short time the intended victim, Robert's junk, had left it far behind.

Undaunted, the remaining four pirate ships gave chase. Before long the leading one was drawing level with the fleeing merchantman. Once again Robert waited until the enemy was almost upon him before firing his shotgun into the crowded decks. The result was the same as on the previous occasion. The pirates lost control of their ship while its victim made good its escape.

The other pirates came alongside their stricken colleague and asked what had gone wrong. There was no point in pressing the attack, they were told. The merchant ship was manned by a devil – a white-faced, red-eyed devil in a long yellow dress who bore a charmed life. Unwilling to challenge the supernatural, the pirates decided to call off the chase. They cast their dead into the sea and set off in search of easier prey.

Meanwhile, on the merchant junk the 'devil' had collapsed from fever and exhaustion. Grateful sailors carried him back to his cabin. On coming round that evening, he found he had only a hazy memory of the day's adventures. When the captain told him what he had done, Robert could hardly believe his ears. 'I'd never have been that brave – or foolish – had I been fully conscious,' he confessed.

'No, Mr Fortune,' smiled the captain. 'Your sickness is our health.'

A week later the junk arrived in Shanghai. Robert, now fully recovered from his illness, packed up the remainder of his samples and arranged for the entire collection to be shipped back to England. After he had seen them safely dispatched, he booked a return passage for himself. Four-and-a-half months later he was back in London.

Sir Horace and his fellow members of the Horticultural Society were delighted with the specimens Robert had collected for them. A special dinner was arranged at which he could be formally thanked. As he was arriving for the celebration, Robert saw a familiar figure climbing the steps ahead of him.

'Lord Tankerton!' he called. 'Your lordship, a word please!'

Tankerton turned. 'Fortune! Excellent to see you. They tell me you've done wonders. Something of a hero, eh?'

Robert felt his cheeks reddening. 'I only did what I was asked to do, sir.'

'Yes, but there are many men who don't. By the way, Fortune, do you remember that business over the guns? Did you actually need them after all?'

'Lord Tankerton,' smiled Robert, 'I owe you my life – and five pounds. Quite a bargain, I think!'

Hernando Cortes

Of all the New World adventurers, none was more daring, brave and ruthlessly cruel than the Spaniard Hernando Cortes (1485–1547). In just three years, heading a party of six hundred men and sixteen horses, he conquered the entire Aztec empire. Here he came across the cocoa bean, which was used as money, and the delicious chocolate drink that the Aztecs made from the beans. He introduced them both into Europe for the first time, so Cortes is probably the man we have to thank for chocolate.

In 1520, during Cortes' struggle with the Aztecs, their emperor Montezuma had been fatally wounded . . .

Listen, my lords! I, Emperor Montezuma of the Aztecs, am dying.

No, don't protest. I can tell from your eyes that you know it's true. I didn't quite believe it myself until this morning. But when the sun rose and sent his glorious light into my room, driving out the darkness and turning all to gold, I knew then that he was calling me to him. Before this day is out, my loyal subjects, your emperor will be one with the Almighty Sun.

Unless it is a trick . . . Is the Almighty flooding the world with brightness to show me what I will be missing when I die? Am I destined for the place of eternal darkness? Perhaps it is what I deserve for failing my people? Deny it not, for it is true! I am a traitor.

I should have seen the truth from the start – but we were all blind as stones. There were signs long before the bearded ones appeared, remember? The waters of the great lake flooded into the city.

Buildings caught fire for no reason. Mysterious voices howled at night, prophesying doom . . . and I thought all this foretold the return of the Glorious God Quetzalcoatl! What a fool I was! It was not a god who came, but a devil. That murderous, cunning devil Señor Hernando Cortes of the land they call 'Spain'.

He looked something like a god, didn't he? Bearded and of pale skin like Quetzalcoatl – it was understandable that I might mistake one for the other. Besides, the fire sticks that killed our men from far off seemed god-like weapons. So did the metal clothes the Spaniards wore, and the great beasts with iron feet upon which they rode. We had never seen the like, so perhaps we might be forgiven for having believed them gods.

The truth came to me in two bright flashes, like the forks of a lightning storm. The first was when the head of a Spaniard my soldiers had killed was brought before me. It was presented on a golden plate, sitting in a pool of dried blood the colour of hot chillies.

Now this Spanish head was huge and covered with beard like a bear. It would not have been out of place on a god. But when I looked closer, I knew it could not be. The eyes, gentlemen, were not the eyes of a god. They were blue and cold, like the mountains before dawn. The mouth below them was a jackal's mouth; tight, narrow and fit only for biting. Maggots were already making their homes in the rotting gums. The blow that killed him must also have smashed out several teeth.

No, I thought, a man like that cannot accompany a god.

My fears were confirmed when I met Cortes himself, the one they had said was Quetzalcoatl returned to Earth.

I arrived at the meeting point in my usual manner, my golden litter carried on the shoulders of nobles. When I descended, the ground before me was strewn with scented flowers so that my imperial feet within their golden sandals should not touch the base and dirty soil. All around my subjects bowed or prostrated themselves to the ground. No one dared look directly at me.

Except that Cortes.

The proud Spaniard jumped from the great beast they call a horse and walked boldly towards me. He was respectful, yes, but not afraid. He gave me some shiny trinket and then extended his arms as if to embrace me. Horrified, my lords stepped forward to prevent such a disgrace. That a man should try to touch me in that way was unheard of, undreamed of even! Yet Cortes tried. I should have seen the truth then, shouldn't I?

The true test came back at my palace, when he was offered food and drink. He ate the meats and the breads well enough; he said our vegetables were the best he had ever tasted. Then he was served with chocolate . . .

That glorious drink, made from the seeds of the cocoa tree and flavoured with vanilla and spices, is, as you know, the nectar of the gods. A dozen brimming jars were prepared for me each day. My royal chocolate was served in golden goblets, each with its own golden spoon. How I adored it! But not Cortes.

The Spaniard had not tasted it before, so I believed it would be a great treat for him. I was wrong. Yes, he made polite sounds and tried to smile, but I could tell it was only pretence. He played with his drink, stirring and scooping and taking only a little at a time. When he refused to have his cup refilled, I knew in my bones that this man meant to do me wrong.

My friends, when I am gone, remember this: never trust a man who dislikes chocolate.

From that moment onwards the truth was clear – but still I did not act. What if I were mistaken? I thought. Perhaps Cortes really was a god, I mused, perhaps he really did like chocolate but was just testing me.

Foolish speculation!

There is someone else in this story, too. I have not mentioned her before, have I? Marina, Cortes' girl, whom he picked up in Tabasco on the coast shortly after he landed. I have as many wives as there are hairs on my head, but somehow this Marina is a different kind of woman. She has something of the witch about her. Perhaps she has learned her evil craft from her master?

At first Marina from Tabasco simply translated the words of Cortes, changing his language into ours. Then she began to add phrases of her own. She flattered me – I was used to that – then she threatened me. When I became angry, she flattered me again. Delightful words slipped from her tongue – words as sweet as my beloved chocolate.

Normally I would have had such a woman taken

away and cut to pieces without a second thought, but Marina was protected by Cortes. He would protect *me* too, she insisted. In these troubled times, she went on, all true force rested with the men from Spain, with their fire sticks and their galloping animals. Rely on them, and I would be more powerful than before. She knew Cortes better than anyone, she told me, and he was good. I must trust her, trust her . . .

Ah well! In the end I did as she wanted. I ignored what I knew to be true and put myself at the mercy of Cortes. And what did he do? He put iron rings and chains about my legs so I was fastened as a common prisoner. Me, the emperor, chained like a beast! How my servants wept and wrapped their cloaks about my legs to stop the rough metal from chafing me! How they begged Cortes to set me free!

What was the point of their pleading? A man who cannot taste the delights of chocolate knows neither pity nor respect.

As I languished in chains, Cortes left the city. He placed the dastardly Pedro de Alvarado in command. What a man! Did I say man? No, he is something worse – a heartless devil. He can never be forgiven for what he did to our people. Let me remind you of his treachery.

Our priests most graciously invited the Spaniards to attend the annual ceremonies in honour of the war god. These were to be performed, as usual, in the holiest of our temples. The young men of my empire's noblest families were to take part. Dressed in their finest robes and feathers, they paraded before the Spaniards like beautiful birds, half of Earth, half of Heaven. Our guests had come into the temple bearing arms, but since they were violent and warlike men, no one thought it strange.

The chants rose into the cloudless sky. The drumming and strumming began, gradually becoming more intense. The dancers pranced and sprang faster and faster. On and on it went – until the murderers struck. Upon a signal from the beast Alvarado, with hideous cries the Spanish fell upon our unarmed youth. The sacred precincts of the temple echoed to the screams of the massacre as young Aztec flesh was stabbed, hacked, pierced and sliced. Neither man nor boy, dancer, musician or priest was spared. The few that made it to the gates were skewered on the pikes of the guards. Down the streets near the temple, they say, blood ran like rainwater after a storm.

I tell you all this again because it brings me to the moment of my greatest shame. No, do not refute me! I may be on the point of leaving you, but my senses are intact. Sit down again and hear my confession.

After the massacre my people rose up against the Spaniards. They wanted me to be set free. There was much fighting and the Spaniards were sore afraid. They were trapped, you see, in a city that hated them. Rats cornered in a barn. I saw the fear in their eyes. I smelled it on their bodies. For the first time since my capture, I felt I had some power.

So when Cortes came crawling to me, I listened. Would I speak to my people? Would I tell them that the Spaniards meant no harm, that the massacre was an accident? No, I would not! Cortes bit his lip as if trying to hold back his anger.

Would I speak to my people if Cortes promised to withdraw from the city? I felt myself growing stronger each minute. 'No!' I replied. 'I will not. I will speak to my people only if you promise that you and all your people will leave my land for ever!'

Cortes hesitated. Reluctantly, he agreed. My finest robes and jewels were brought and I was dressed in them. I made my way onto the battlements, escorted by Spanish soldiers. Having been told that their emperor would address them, a great multitude of Aztecs had assembled below. When they saw me, some cried out in delight, others fell down in humble respect and worship.

A profound silence fell upon all who were present and I began to speak.

I was not a prisoner, I lied. Cortes and his men were my guests. At this, someone shouted out that I was a traitor. Undaunted, I pressed on. The Spaniards would leave the moment they were permitted to do so, I explained. More people were shouting abuse at me now. A stone was thrown, then another. All Cortes wants, I cried, is a clear and safe pathway through the streets . . .

An arrow struck me in the leg. As I bent down to pull it out, another hit me in the neck. By now stones and arrows were falling all around me. I collapsed to the ground, filled with the ghastly realization of what I had done. Montezuma, the

emperor and defender of the Aztecs, had committed the gravest crime of all.

In agreeing to help his enemies, he had betrayed his people.

There, I have said it all now. You may shake your heads, but I know it to be true. And in death I have my just deserts.

Dear gentlemen, I thank you for staying with me to the end. I am very tired now. I am almost gone. My wounds are hurting still, but the pain is growing less. It is being eased in preparation for my entry into that land where there is no pain. The place of light perpetual, of gardens, flowers and brilliant birds that sing without ceasing.

Farewell, then, my beloved Aztecs. I pity you whom I leave behind. Had I strength enough I would weep, for I have left you in the cruel hands of a widow-maker who scorns the delicious taste of chocolate.

Sir Joseph Banks

In 1768 twenty five-year-old Joseph Banks paid £10,000 of his own money (an absolutely huge sum in those days) to take a scientific party on board Captain Cook's Endeavour. The ship was sailing on a voyage of exploration to Tahiti in the Pacific Ocean. The voyage became even longer than planned when Cook travelled on to New Zealand and the east coast of Australia, and ended up circumnavigating the world. Banks was a passionate botanist, eager to discover plants unknown in the

West. His three-year voyage, although yielding over eight hundred new species, had moments of extreme danger . . .

The first disaster hit Banks' party in Tierra del Fuego, a painfully bleak island at the tip of South America. On a day that dawned bright, if not warm, Banks led a group inland to examine the local flora. In mid-afternoon the weather changed. An icy wind came up from the south, driving sharp flurries of snow before it. At the same time another disaster hit. One of the party's artists (a crucial member of the team in the days before photography) had an epileptic fit.

Banks had little experience of such conditions, nor had he been trained how to cope in an emergency. After a good deal of floundering about and a night outdoors in near-polar conditions, two of the party's servants were discovered frozen to death. The remainder of the group survived by eating raw vulture. This was a useful introduction to an exotic diet that over the course of the voyage would include kangaroo, shark, albatross, rat and dog.

From South America the *Endeavour* sailed into the broad Pacific. When they reached Tahiti, Banks had further difficulties, this time more human than meteorological. The island was as close to paradise as one could find on earth. The climate was warm and balmy, the vegetation luscious, and the people friendly – especially the women. Banks' only regret was that Tahitian houses had no walls, so there was no opportunity of sneaking out of sight with a local beauty.

Shortly afterwards a more serious difficulty arose. The Tahitians lived a free and easy existence, willingly sharing all they possessed. Not so the Europeans from the *Endeavour* with their tradition of private property. They were easily angered, therefore, when they discovered their prize possessions were being filched by the natives. Banks, educated at public school and Oxford University, was a natural diplomat. He spent more time than he wanted to sorting out disputes between the locals and the crew of the *Endeavour*.

From Tahiti Captain Cook sailed the ship south then east. After a voyage of several weeks he encountered land straight ahead. Neither he nor anyone else on board knew what country it was. Banks thought it was *Terra Australis*, a mysterious continent that King George III had secretly asked

Cook to explore. Cook himself was not so sure. Having studied the records left by Dutch explorers, he believed *Terra Australis* lay further to the west. In the end, Cook was proved right. The land was New Zealand. The *Endeavour* made the first ever circumnavigation of the country and showed that it was not one but two separate islands.

New Zealand provided Banks with another wonderful array of plant specimens. Gathering them, however, was a risky business as the native Maoris were often less than friendly. Banks, always keen to establish amicable relations where possible, was deeply distressed when the ship's crew shot dead local warriors who were trying to steal their muskets. But he later took a more lenient attitude towards such self-defence when, in a different part of the island, he learned that it was customary for some Maoris to cook and eat enemies captured in battle.

These trials and tribulations were nothing compared with what came next. From New Zealand the *Endeavour* headed west. Once again it found a land mass ahead and Cook and Banks puzzled over what it could be. There was only one way to find out, they decided, and that was to follow the coastline and see where it led.

At first the sailing was fair. The barren shoreline gave way to the rich green of a broad bay. Banks was delighted and named it Botany Bay because of the many flora he found there. From here the *Endeavour* made its way north, stopping from time to time to put Banks and his team ashore to gather further samples of the remarkable plant life. After a couple of weeks, it was quite clear that the land they had encountered was no mere island. It was part of the famous *Terra Australis*, Cook realized. Simplified to 'Australia', the name stuck, although at one stage there was a suggestion that it might be changed to 'Banksia'.

By early June 1770, some six weeks after reaching Australia, their progress had slowed considerably. The vessel had entered a region of islands and reefs that seemed to go on for ever. Neither Cook nor any member of the crew had ever seen anything like it before. Although they did not know it, they were in the middle of what we now know as the Great Barrier Reef.

The reef is spectacularly beautiful. Most lovely of all are its underwater fantasy cities of multicoloured coral. To the sailor, though, the banks of knife-edged coral lurking just beneath the glittering surface of the sea are hideous perils. If a wooden sailing ship strikes one at speed, its hull is ripped open and it sinks almost immediately.

Cook knew full well the danger he was in. Sails were taken in and the *Endeavour* slowed to a walking pace. Extra lookouts hung over the bows. When the passage became narrower and more shallow, one of the ship's small boats was lowered and sent ahead with poles to sound out the depth. Slowly, mile by painstaking mile, the *Endeavour* crept into the unknown along the uncharted shore of eastern Australia.

Progress was most dangerous by moonlight, when the jagged spears of coral were difficult to see. So it was that on the night of 10 June 1770, all aboard the *Endeavour* heard the vicious tearing they had so dreaded. Their ship was aground on the reef.

It was high tide. Cook knew that as the waters fell the ship's position would become more desperate by the minute. Speed was essential. Men were immediately ordered below to assess the damage and, if necessary, man the ship's pumps.

At the same time, the small boats were launched and attached to the stern by stout ropes. To assist them, an anchor was dropped some distance behind. The captain hoped that hauling it in would drag his ship into deeper water.

When all was ready, the men in the boats began rowing for all they were worth. The sea foamed beneath their oars. On board the capstan crew sweated and cursed to wind in the anchor.

The *Endeavour* moved not an inch.

Daylight revealed the true horror of their position. The shore, brown and inhospitable, was twenty-five miles to their west. No man could possibly reach it by swimming. That meant using the boats, but these did not have sufficient room for even half the crew. The captain would have to decide whom to take and whom to leave behind – not an enviable choice. Besides, even if the boats reached the shore, there was little chance of survival there and certainly no hope of ever being rescued.

No, Cook decided, there was no point in abandoning the ship. The *Endeavour* was their only hope of survival. The vessel and its crew were thousands of miles from the nearest European trading post in a place not on any map and never before visited by any outsider. Either they all stayed

together and tried to rescue their ship, or they all died.

As the tide fell, the *Endeavour* settled more firmly on its spiky perch. It was as if a spear had been thrust into its chest, threatening its very heart. The timbers groaned and growled under the strain. When the sea began to rise again, the gush of water through the hole in the planking increased alarmingly. It was all the hand-operated pumps could do to keep the ship from filling.

Meanwhile, to lighten the vessel and increase its chances of floating free at high tide, Cook ordered all surplus weight to be cast over the side. Tons of ballast were dragged up from the bilges and thrown into the sea. Six guns splashed overboard. Most painful of all was ditching the barrels of drinking water – even if the weather remained calm so the ship was not broken up in a storm, the crew would die of thirst unless they broke free from the coral claws that held them.

Cook's calculations proved correct. Several tons lighter, at high tide the *Endeavour* lifted clear. Nevertheless, the ordeal was far from over. No sooner had the cheers of the crew died away than fresh cries were heard. They came from the men working the pumps. Now she was afloat, the *Endeavour* was taking in water at a terrifying rate. An attempt was made to patch the leak, but a satisfactory repair needed to be made from the outside and that could be done only with the ship out of the water. Meanwhile, working flat out, the pumps could just stem the tide. If one of them failed, the *Endeavour* would sink.

The pumps did not fail. If anything, it was the dry-mouthed crew who were most likely to give out. To help them Cook ordered everyone on board to take their turn on the handles. Banks and his botanists, hands blistered and bleeding from the unaccustomed labour, took their turn along with the rest.

Carefully, very carefully, Cook guided his stricken ship up the coast. Six days later he found an estuary that led to a broad river with gently sloping banks. Here the *Endeavour* was run aground so that the damage to the hull could be investigated and repaired.

The carpenter who first set eyes on the hole let out a cry of surprise. 'Captain!' he called. 'Come here, if you would, sir. I reckon it's a miracle.'

Cook made his way to where the man was

standing. A broad wound had been slashed in the ship's hull. Remarkably, though, the hole was not empty. In it, blocking half the gap, was wedged a broken piece of coral. The source of their misery had also been their salvation.

'Well I never!' smiled Cook. 'If that hadn't been there, the water would have poured in and we'd have sunk like a stone. Yes, I suppose you could say it is something of a miracle.'

Ferdinand Magellan

*T*he Portuguese sailor Ferdinand Magellan
(c. 1480–1521) led the first circumnavigation
of the world. Leaving Spain with five ships, he
discovered the strait at the foot of South America
that now bears his name. His crossing of the calm
Southern Sea, which his sailors re-named the 'Pacific'
or 'Peaceful' Ocean, is one of the great tales of
human endurance. The Spanish captain Juan
Sebastian Elcano (d.1526) took command when
Magellan was killed in the Philippines. Assisted by

the seventeen surviving crew members, he guided home a single battered vessel, the Vittoria, *laden with priceless spices from the Orient.*

On 12 April 1518, twenty-five-year-old Master Andrew of Bristol, a ship's gunner, married Isabella Herrera of Seville. The parents of the Spanish bride were delighted at the match and welcomed the young Englishman into their family as if he were their own son. Gunners were well paid, and after a few voyages Andrew could expect to make enough to retire from the sea and set up Isabella and himself in a small farm of their own in Spain.

Andrew's parents-in-law were very pleased, therefore, when the following year he told them he was joining the *Trinidad*, one of five ships sailing under the Portuguese captain Ferdinand Magellan with instructions to discover the westward sea route to the Spice Islands of south-east Asia. Magellan had royal backing, which was a good start. Moreover, as everyone knew, the Spice Islands were the source of unimaginable riches. The plants that grew there – nutmeg, allspice, cinnamon, cardamom, cloves and peppercorns – all fetched huge sums of money in Europe. If all went well, Andrew would be able to buy that farm on his return – several years earlier than anticipated.

Having bade farewell to his young wife and their infant son, Andrew went on board the *Trinidad* on 18 September. Two days later the fleet of five ships left Sanlucar de Barrameda and set course for Tenerife.

Andrew was a popular member of the crew and the first year of the voyage went well for him. He did not take part in the mutiny that led to the execution of one of the Spanish captains, nor was he on board the *Santiago* when it was wrecked at the mouth of the River Santa Cruz. For the desertion of the *San Antonio* some weeks later he had nothing but scorn. His faith in Magellan, whose fleet was now down to three ships, was absolute. 'If I stick with that man,' he told his best friend Pedro Toribio, 'this time next year I'll be ploughing my fields and coming home every evening to my wife and family.'

Like his iron-willed commander, Andrew broke into tears of joy when the *Trinidad* emerged from what they then called the Patagonian Strait and entered the South Sea alongside the *Concepcion* and the *Vittoria*. Their journey to the land rich in plants where they would gather their fortunes was surely almost complete. Had he known what lay ahead, he might have remained dry-eyed. They were entering upon weeks of torture in which every ounce of drinkable water, even a tear-drop, would be worth its weight in gold.

For three weeks the ships sailed up the coast of Chile. Shortly before Christmas, Magellan gave the order to turn north-west, leaving the land behind them and heading for their final destination, which the captain believed to be no more than a few hundred miles away. A warm breeze filled the ships' sails and the welcome absence of storms led to the sailors renaming the deep, peaceful ocean around them the 'Pacific'.

After a month's sailing, land was sighted. Sure that he was now close to the Spice Islands, Magellan decided not to go ashore for fresh provisions but to press on towards his goal. When February arrived and there was still no sign of the voyage ending, the crew were getting desperate.

By now the *Trinidad*'s supply of drinking water was all but gone. What remained, a few inches slopping around in the bottom of a barrel, was covered with yellow-green slime. Men fought each other to catch the morning dew that fell from the sails. The supplies of dried meat had long since given out. The cook, a plump man back in Spain but now reduced to a mere skeleton, cut up strips of ox hide and gave it to the men to chew. Chewing, however, was almost impossible.

Deprived of fresh fruit and vegetables, the sailors were stricken by scurvy. Their hair turned dry as hay and came out in handfuls. Joints ached and swelled. Gums bled profusely for no obvious reason and the teeth within them became so loose they could be pulled out with fingers. Trying to chew on the tough ox hide, Andrew found himself spitting out his own teeth.

Rats gnawed their way into the biscuit barrels and devoured their contents. All that remained was a foul-smelling and worm-infested paste of crumbs and rodent urine. Almost every day a member of the crew died and their wasted body was cast over the side with scant, muttered prayers.

After seventy days at sea the cook and his assistant began catching the rats that lived in the bilges and cooking them over the brick stove on deck. The smell of fresh meat almost drove the starving men insane and an officer had to stand guard over the oven with his sword drawn. Ten days later the cook announced that he had caught the last rat. From now on it was stinking biscuit or nothing.

Andrew the gunner did not believe the cook. One afternoon, sleeping down below out of the heat of the sun, he was sure he heard the squeak of a rat coming from the bilges beneath him. He wondered what to do. As it would be almost impossible to catch the animal on his own, he went up on deck. His friend Pedro was gazing at the great curve of the horizon.

'Hungry?' Andrew asked quietly.

'Is that some sort of English joke, Andrew? I could almost eat my own arm.'

'No need for that, Pedro. Listen.'

After Andrew had explained about what he had heard, the two men slipped down into the bilges without anyone noticing. Standing on the stone ballast, they waited for their eyes to become accustomed to the darkness. The stench of rotting waste and rat droppings was utterly revolting. Hunger, though, gave them an almost superhuman determination.

'Right!' whispered Andrew when he could just

about make out the shape of the timbers around him. 'I'll chuck a stone and see if it disturbs the little beggar.'

He picked up a pebble and threw it into the far corner. Nothing happened. He tried again, this time landing the stone in the opposite corner. Still nothing happened. But the third time he tried, he was rewarded with a scuttling sound along the hull to their left. Pedro made a move towards it.

'No!' hissed Andrew. 'You stay here. I'll go round the back.'

'What do we do when we catch it?'

'Eat it, of course!'

'Yes, but what about cooking?'

'I've thought of that. We'll skin it and keep it down here in a bowl of salt water. It'll end up cured like bacon, then we can sneak back down and have the feast of our lives!'

Pedro sighed. 'I can almost taste it already. Like bacon!'

Andrew crept to the other side of the ship and moved in behind the spot where they had heard the scuttling. Advancing quietly as a cat, he closed in for the kill.

When Andrew was no more than a metre away

from it, the rat shot towards Pedro. The sailor stuck out his foot to block its path. The rat immediately doubled back. Andrew made a grab with his right hand. His fingers clasped tight around a body of warm flesh and fur. At the same time, sharp teeth bit his finger to the bone. He didn't feel the pain. With a quick twist of his free hand, he broke the animal's neck.

'Got it?' whispered Pedro.

Andrew did not reply.

'I asked whether you managed to catch it!'

Even as he was speaking, Pedro became aware of a horrible tearing sound. Oh my God, he thought. I don't believe it!

'Andrew! Andrew! What are you doing? You're not . . . eating it, are you? Not like that. Not raw!'

The noise stopped for a moment. From out of the hellish darkness of the bilges came a voice Pedro scarcely recognized: 'Forgive me, my friend. I just couldn't wait.'

As the repulsive tearing and cracking began again, Pedro turned and climbed wearily back to the deck.

Later that afternoon Andrew the gunner was struck down with violent stomach pains and uncontrollable vomiting. He died an hour later and his emaciated body was committed to the deep just as the sun was setting over the vast emptiness of the ocean. ·

RISKING DEATH FOR
RHODODENDRONS

Sir Joseph Hooker

J oseph Hooker (1817–1911) was perhaps the greatest of all nineteenth-century botanists. He lived during the reign of Queen Victoria, when the British Empire was at its height. He was much respected by many of the great scientists of his day, including Charles Darwin, and he was almost as passionate about exploration as he was about seeking new species of plant. Personally, he was a tough, sometimes arrogant man with a firm belief in the right of the British to have a world-wide empire.

Sir Joseph Hooker did not reply to the question immediately. Instead, he selected a cigar from the box on the table before him and handed it to an attendant to prepare.

'Difficult one, that,' confessed Sir Joseph eventually. 'I've had many tricky moments during my travels. But the most dangerous . . . ?' He took the cigar back and stuck it between his teeth. 'Yes, it was probably with Archibald Campbell, back in forty-nine.' He spoke between puffs as the attendant applied a match to the blunt end of his cigar. 'There was a moment when I really thought my time was up.'

The cigar was now well alight. Settling back into his leather armchair, Sir Joseph blew a cloud of smoke into the air and watched it rise slowly towards the yellow ceiling of the billiard room. 'Mmm!' He closed his eyes for a moment, casting his memory back forty years. 'Quite a close run thing it was. Must have told you about it before, though?'

When his companion said he'd never heard the story but would love to do so, Sir Joseph smiled. 'Well, I don't mind running through it once more. As long as you promise not to fall asleep!'

*

I was in Sikkim – you know, north-east frontier of India, Chinese border, Himalayas and all that. Wonderful place. Roof of the world. Right up in the mountains, at around fourteen thousand feet, I found literally dozens of species of rhododendron unknown outside the region. Stunningly beautiful they were – and such scent!

Anyway, it's not the rhododendrons you want to hear about, is it? No, I thought not. Well, travelling around Sikkim was not very easy in those days. Not only were there no roads to speak of, but the Rajah – the king, that is – was under the influence of a particularly anti-British 'Dewan' – that's the local word for minister. I can't recall the fellow's name. We just called him the 'deadly Dewan'. He felt he had some sort of mission to keep the British from taking over his tinpot territory. Not a hope, of course.

Now, as you know, I'm not a political man myself, but I do believe all subjects of Queen Victoria deserve to be treated decently wherever they are in the world. Shown proper respect. The deadly Dewan did just the opposite. He went out of his way to make my plant-collecting in Sikkim as difficult as possible. You wouldn't believe it, but he actually chopped down bridges that he knew we wanted to cross. As for food, there were places where it couldn't be bought for a king's ransom.

When I got back to base and mentioned this to the authorities, they were hopping mad. They insisted that Archibald Campbell accompany me on my return to Sikkim, to see what was going on. Archie was the British political wallah for that region. Honest sort of chap. Knew his stuff, too.

At first we didn't have any trouble, although we did have an unnerving feeling that we were being watched. Which we were, of course – as you'll see.

Sir Joseph, eyes bright, was now leaning forward in his chair. He was so wrapped up in his storytelling that he had forgotten all about his cigar. Neglected, it had burned out in an ashtray.

One afternoon we reached the village of Chumanako. It was a remote place, thousands of feet up and bitterly cold. Shown a hut where we might stay, Archie and I went in to see if it was suitable. No sooner were we inside than half a dozen burly locals – policemen of some sort, I think – joined us. I didn't fancy spending the night with them, so I went back outside to find a spot to pitch the tents.

Well, just as I left the hut all hell was let loose inside. There were shouts and grunts and crashes, and through it all came the voice of Archie yelling that he was being murdered!

I dashed back inside to find that the thugs had shoved my companion to the floor, beaten him and were now trussing him up like a Christmas goose. Good heavens! I thought. There's going to be an awful stink – no one treats a British diplomat like that and gets away with it!

I learned later that the deadly Dewan's thinking went like this: seize an important British citizen, smash him about a bit or even kill him, and the government wallahs back in London will take fright and leave Sikkim well alone. In other words, poor old Archie, because he was a politician, was being made an example of.

When I realized what was going on, I tried to get to my friend. I was met with a vicious punch or two and pinned to the wall. The Dewan's men were hefty chaps, armed to the teeth and pretty evil-looking. I decided that further resistance was useless. Even so, I would make a protest. If they were taking

Archie prisoner, I insisted on going along too.

At first they wouldn't hear of it and tried to push me away. But after a while they gave up and let me walk with them. My decision might have saved Archie's life, you never know. Anyway, a strange sight we were: a British diplomat tied up and hauled along behind a mule, a bespectacled British botanist walking beside him, and the pair surrounded by ferocious-looking Bhutanese men.

We were taken to Tumloong. Not wanting to waste the journey, as we went along I gathered rhododendron seeds from beside the path. In the capital we were imprisoned in a hut. It was bitterly cold, especially at night, and the food was ghastly. Once some official or other came in and said we were both going to be executed as spies the following morning. I didn't sleep much that night, I must confess.

It was just a threat, thank God! After three weeks in this freezing hell-hole I managed to get us out. Since I wasn't really a prisoner but was there simply because I refused to abandon Archie, they gave me some privileges. One of these was writing letters. I wrote dozens, one of which eventually got through to the Governor-General of India, my old friend Lord Dalhousie.

His lordship didn't waste much time. Soldiers and artillery were rushed up to the frontier with Sikkim. The message was clear: hand over your prisoners or the British Army is coming in!

This really put the wind up the deadly Dewan. He ordered that we be escorted to the frontier immediately and handed over to our own people. It all went without a hitch. We were back in Darjeeling for Christmas.

Sir Joseph looked down at his extinguished cigar. 'That, old chap, is just about the end of the story.' He signalled to the attendant to bring over a box of matches. 'Except that what I read in *The Times* the other day makes a rather fitting postscript. The Rajah of Sikkim has agreed that a British diplomat should be a permanent political adviser at his court. You know what that means, don't you? It means Britain has finally taken over Sikkim. About time too, I say!'

Marianne North

M arianne North (1830–1890) was not a typical Victorian spinster. For fifteen years after the death of her father she travelled the world painting and writing about the multitude of wonderful plants she came across. Her priceless collection of over eight hundred paintings is now housed in the Marianne North Gallery, Kew Gardens, London. No jungle was too thick for Marianne, no mountain pass too high, no road too muddy. Compared with her overseas adventures, life back home could be very dull . . .

'One minute I was gazing at the tail of the mule in front of me, the next it had quite disappeared!' Marianne's eyes twinkled with amusement as she recalled the incident.

Leaning forward in her chair, Aunt Emily let out a little cry of excitement. 'Dear me, Marianne! What on earth had happened to the poor donkey? I do hope it was not hurt!'

Marianne smiled. 'It was a mule, Aunt, not a donkey. And no, it wasn't hurt. At least, not badly. I believe it might have had sore ears where I pulled them.'

Aunt Emily collapsed back into her chair with astonishment and Uncle Edward took over the questioning. 'Well I never! What were you up to this time, Marianne, pulling a mule's ears? It doesn't sound very respectable!'

'It wasn't, Uncle. But in conditions like those we found ourselves in, everyone had to lend a hand, lady or not. Listen, I'll tell you what occurred. I know you'll find it fun.'

The incident in question had happened when Marianne was on the road to Minas in upcountry Brazil. After a week of torrential rain the state of the dirt track was appalling, churned to a broad ribbon of squelching mud by the hooves and feet of hundreds of travellers. It was worse than a ploughed field and a good deal more treacherous. In places the ruts in the track were like ponds – if a mule or even a person slipped into one of the deeper ones, they could easily drown. To prevent this happening, a guide walked ahead of the mules with a pole to test the depth of the murky mud holes.

It was getting late and the exhausted man was eager to press ahead to Minas before nightfall. Glancing quickly at a pool to his left, he decided it did not present a danger and, judging it not worth testing, moved on to the next one. Had he examined it more closely, he would have found it some three feet deep and filled with a greasy paste the colour of chocolate.

A few seconds later, the mule in front of Marianne's, the one carrying her personal belongings, suddenly lost its footing and disappeared from sight.

Marianne immediately pulled on the reins of her mount and brought it to a halt. By now the leading mule, covered from hoof to head in mud, was splashing and sliding in a vain attempt to climb out of the hole.

Marianne quickly saw what was wrong and told the servants to unload the floundering beast. Without a weight on its back, she believed, it would be able to climb free. The plan was unsuccessful. Even without its burden, the mule was unable to scale the slippery sides of its pen. At this point, two of the servants grabbed the mule's tail and tried to haul it out backwards. The action produced much loud braying but no movement.

'There is only one solution,' Marianne announced, climbing off her own mount into the ankle-deep mud, 'we will have to lift it out.'

'Lift it?' chorused the rest of the party.

'Yes, lift it!' retorted Marianne. She began giving orders. 'You two climb in to the pit and get your hands underneath the animal's belly. Fernando and Domenico get hold of the tail. Pedro and I will seize it by the ears.'

'You, Miss North?' exclaimed Domenico in disbelief.

Marianne gave him a stern glance. 'And why not? I may be a lady but that does not mean I'm completely useless!' She paddled across to the pit,

bent down and grabbed the trapped mule by one of its long, rough ears.

It took ten minutes to lift the animal clear. The first time they tried, it fell back into the pool with a splash that cascaded foul smelling liquid over all its would-be rescuers. When the creature finally scrambled free, every inch of Marianne, including her face and hands, was covered in a thick coating of dark slime.

Seeing this extraordinary sight, one of the servants said with a grin, 'Why, Miss North, you brown like us now!'

Marianne grinned back at him. 'How splendid!' she replied. 'I'm glad that's one less difference between us.'

As she finished her story, Marianne lifted her eyes from the fire and looked towards the window. February rain slapped sadly against the panes. Beyond, across the grey lawn, the limbs of the brown-black elms strained in the gusty wind. Oh dear, she thought, England really was no place to be at this time of year. It was almost as dreary as the company in the room.

As if trying to prove Marianne right, Aunt Emily

leaned forward in her chair and said politely, 'That was so thrilling, Marianne dear! What a brave young lady you are! Do tell us more about those wonderful people you encountered in Brazil. And the lovely plants and trees! It all sounds *so* interesting!'

Uncle Edward stretched out a lean white hand towards the watercress sandwiches cut like postage stamps. 'Thrilling tales, Marianne! Do give us another.'

Miss Spindlebury and Mrs Thurlow, who had been sitting as stiff and silent as the pillars of Stonehenge, added their voices to the chorus. 'Another story, Miss North, please!'

Marianne turned back into the room and smiled. 'If it would please you, of course. I'd be delighted.' She put her cup and saucer back on the low table before her.

'I don't think I have told you about the caves of Corvelho in Brazil, have I? Well, they are one of the most wondrous sights I have ever seen. The entrances are all set about with gigantic creepers and cacti, and when we approached, a flock of lovely white owls swooped out over our heads.'

As she talked, in her mind's eye Marianne saw again the cavern as vast as a cathedral, fifty yards high, dripping with gleaming stalactites in blue and green and cream. She remembered the journey home by mule, trotting through the moonlight in a cloud of white dust, the fireflies in the silk-cotton trees burning like stars.

Then came their arrival in the strange-sounding settlement of Once, whose two dozen citizens rushed outside and stared at them in amazement. They had never seen Englishwomen before, let alone two travel-stained spinsters riding down the main street on mules at eight o'clock at night. The welcome was warm, though. A very fat lady, whose whole body wobbled when she walked, gave a smile as broad as a melon and said she had 'lovely accommodation for fine ladies'.

Marianne soon realized that 'lovely accommodation' did not mean the same in Once as in Rio de Janeiro. She and her travelling companion, Mary, were housed in a barn used for weaving. Half the tiles were missing from the roof and the wind whistled like a runaway train through the cracks in the walls. When Mary asked the fat lady what happened when it rained, she roared with laughter and slapped her hands on her broad thighs. 'What a question, lady!' she hooted. 'Why, when it rains we all get wet!'

The more she talked about her experiences, the further Marianne drifted from the tight little circle of the tea party. She had moved from the windy barn to the tiny inn kept by the aged Donna Anna. The rooms were filled with aromatic sacks of grain and bales of vegetables, but the beds were as spotlessly white and fluffy as the clouds that hung over the dense green hilltops surrounding the town.

Caught up in her story, Marianne was transported to the exotic jungle. Her senses were overwhelmed. The great trees soaring above, luxurious orchids hanging across the path, brilliant insects, scents and smells that took one's breath away, and all around creatures crawling, climbing, slithering – everything was so alive, so vigorous, so beautiful, so new.

Marianne stopped speaking for a moment. Words failed her. She was simply unable to describe the wonders she had seen. 'I tried to paint what met my eyes, of course,' she explained softly, 'but I could not do it justice. The land, the vegetation, the people – all beyond words!' She was far away now, lying back in one of Donna Anna's huge white beds, listening to the sounds of the tropical night outside.

The thin voice of Uncle Edward cut into her reverie. 'And do you really enjoy the company of those sorts of people, Miss North? You know, the rough and inelegant types?'

Without thinking, Marianne replied quietly, 'Oh yes, indeed. I would much rather spend my time with less civilized and more interesting people.'

Uncle Edward exchanged a shocked glance with his wife. No one spoke.

Realizing what she had said and not wishing to give offence, Marianne added hastily, 'I mean, the company of more primitive peoples is sometimes, er, a welcome change. Just once in a while, of course.'

'Of course,' echoed Miss Spindlebury.

There was another awkward silence. Eventually, Aunt Emily grasped the handle of the teapot. 'More tea, Marianne?' Her voice was sharper and shinier than a cake slice.

'No thank you, Aunt.' Marianne did her best to smile. 'Look at the hour! Dear me! I think perhaps it is time I went.'

And not just from this tea party, she thought. It is high time I set sail for distant lands once more.

John Tradescant

J ohn Tradescant (c. 1570–1638) and his son, also named John (1608–1662), were gardeners to King Charles I. They did much more than dig, prune and plant, however. Both were keen collectors of unusual flora and fauna, and travelled widely in search of interesting species. While civil war was raging in England, the younger Tradescant was combing the colony of Virginia in America for new items for the family collection.

Seated at the end of the parlour furthest from the fire, a pair of uncouth-looking men sat drinking and watching John Tradescant as he ate his evening meal. From time to time one of them leaned across to his companion and whispered something. At one point, when the landlord was out of the room, the younger of the two started to get to his feet. His partner laid a hand on his shoulder and thrust him back into his seat.

'Wait,' he said softly. 'Our time will come.'

The square shouldered plant-hunter sat at his customary table beside the fireplace seemingly unaware of the attentions of his fellow guests. While waiting for his meal he had called for pen and ink and started to make a list on a sheet of paper he drew from his pocket. He had paused occasionally, looking up at the grimy wooden ceiling as if trying to remember something. After the landlord had brought his meal he continued to write, slicing a mouthful of turkey then exchanging knife for pen to add a new item to his growing catalogue.

John was still working long after his wooden platter had been removed and his mug refilled from the oak barrel resting on a trestle beneath the stairs. His watchers, who had been drinking steadily all evening, were still there too. Moonlight filtered through the cracks in the shuttered window and lit their scarred faces. Owls hooted in the distant Virginian woods.

Eventually, the landlord decided he could wait up no longer. 'If you'll be so good as to excuse me, gentlemen, I will retire. My boy here will see to your needs.' He gave a friendly wave in the direction of a pale-faced youth of about fourteen who was curled up asleep on a bed of rushes. 'I bid you goodnight, gentlemen.'

John looked up from his writing. 'Landlord? Before you leave us, would you be so good as to bring me another candle? I fear this one will last scarcely half an hour.' Noticing the slight frown that flitted across the inn-keeper's brow, he added, 'I will pay the usual rate, of course.'

The landlord disappeared. When he returned a few moments later, bearing a fresh candle, he glanced suspiciously across at his other two customers. He had seen them before. They had been in the colony a year now, making a living as trappers. The gossip was that they were wrongdoers, fugitives from English law. To the landlord, a shrewd judge of character, it sounded plausible enough. Although he could not afford to turn them away, he did not like them. Such rough men gave his public house a bad name.

'You'll be all right here, Mr Tradescant?' he enquired as he set the candle down on the table.

'Certainly, landlord. I have everything a man could wish for.' John stroked his beard and sighed. 'Though I miss my dear wife, of course.'

The landlord nodded. 'Of course, sir.' With a slight bow and another glance in the direction of the trappers, he walked heavily upstairs. Undisturbed, his son slept soundly on.

As soon as the landlord was out of sight, John bent down, picked up a wooden box from the floor and placed it on the bench beside him. Still writing, with his left hand he opened the lid and felt inside. He then pulled his cloak closer about him so that it fell across the open box, hiding it completely. He did all this without once lifting his eyes from the paper in front of him.

The trappers rose to their feet. John glanced towards them and nodded. 'Goodnight, sirs. Sleep well.'

'We ain't going to sleep, Tradescant,' growled the

older man. He crossed the room and stood directly in front of John's table. 'Not till we got what we want, any road.'

'Got what you want? Can I be of any assistance?' John had laid down his pen and placed his hands on the table before him. His eyes were bright and alert.

'You know what we want. Don't make it difficult, Tradescant. Just hand it over and you won't get hurt.'

John sighed. 'Really, sir! There is no point in threatening me. I have no idea what you are talking about.'

The younger man, who had been checking that the boy was still asleep, strode quickly to the table. 'Don't give me that rubbish, mister! We know why you go out in them woods for days. Same as we know what you have in them boxes you come back with.'

'Of course you know what's in my boxes! It's no secret. They contain plants and seeds for my collection. For the King's gardens.'

The man leaned forward so that his stubbled face was only inches from John's. His breath had the odour of dung. 'Seeds! King's garden! You don't think anyone believes that rubbish, do you? It's silver, isn't it? You've found a little seam of silver which you're mining on the quiet.'

While the man was speaking, John leaned back so that his shoulders now rested against the log wall behind him. His hands remained outstretched before him.

'And we've found you out,' continued the older man. As he spoke he drew out a long knife from inside his coat and pointed it towards John's chest. 'So just come outside with us, unlock the door of the shed where it's hid – and we'll not hurt you. On the other hand, if you don't co-operate we'll just have to lift the key from you—'

'And my friend is an expert at lifting keys,' interjected his companion. 'He does it with his knife. It's not pretty, but it works. Oh yes! It works real nice. Every time.'

The sound of threats caused the boy to stir in his sleep. Alarmed, the knife-bearer glanced anxiously towards him.

John seized the moment. With a loud cry of 'Help!' he braced himself against the wall, slid his hands to the edge of the table and pushed it away from him with all his strength. It crashed to the floor. Ink, paper, pen and candle tumbled after it. The force sent the thieves staggering backwards. Before they could recover, John's left hand had reached into the box beside him and emerged with a flintlock pistol.

He pointed the gun at his assailants. 'It is primed, sirs, and I will have no hesitation in using it if you come one step closer.'

The boy, woken by the commotion, stared about him in wide-eyed disbelief. From the room above came the voice of the landlord wondering what the devil was going on.

The thieves froze, unsure what to do. For a second John thought they might try and rush him. He had never shot a man before and did not want to do so now.

Fortunately, hearing the tread of the landlord on the stairs, the villains saw the hopelessness of their position. With a stream of curses, they turned, ran to the door and fled into the night.

'What in the name of heaven was all that about, Mr Tradescant?' asked the landlord, closing the front door and bolting it.

John lowered his pistol and sat down. 'Just a little misunderstanding, landlord. Those villains seemed to be under the impression that I am here to collect silver.'

'I had heard that rumour myself, sir, though I did my best to quash it.' The innkeeper thought for a moment before adding, 'It seems it started with something you once said when you were leaving on one of your forest trips. You spoke of silver then, sir.'

John looked confused. 'Silver? Silver?' Suddenly, his face lightened and he gave a loud laugh. 'Ha! I remember now! Someone asked me what I did in the woods all day, and I replied that I was earning the King's wages – although I said 'silver' instead of wages. Yes, that was it! I said I was earning the King's silver! Haha! To think that remark could have cost me my life.'

Still chuckling, John put his pistol carefully back in its box. 'Well, landlord, it's clearly time for me to return home before my seeds of silver get us into any more trouble.'

David Douglas

T*he intrepid Scotsman David Douglas (1799–1834) was employed by the Royal Horticultural Society of London to scour the wilds of North America for plants, flowers and trees unknown in Britain. His flora hunting, often carried out in the most atrocious of conditions, was tremendously successful. The Society received over two hundred new species as a result, including the Douglas fir.*

During my first twenty-five years on earth I had but one love. I cared for neither wealth nor possessions. Fine food and drink meant little to me, and I had no time for the ladies. What made my Scottish heart sing with joy was the sheer beauty of God's natural world.

Alas! Had I only remained true to my first love, I would not have been so utterly wretched as I am now.

I can remember the exact day, hour and minute of my fall. I was feasting with a good friend of mine, Chief Cockqua of the Chenook and Chochalii tribes that inhabit the land near Fort Vancouver, Canada. A great feast it was, too – a whole giant sturgeon, many feet long, freshly caught and cooked over an open fire in a manner known only to the Chenook peoples.

The last of the fish had been consumed. Night was falling and the pungent smell of birch hung in the still air. My hosts and I were seated round the embers of a huge fire, telling stories. A fantastically carved pipe of local tobacco was passed slowly between the men. I had just handed this pipe to my left when I looked up and saw, on the other side of the fire, a young face that was new to me. It was

Laughing Water, Cockqua's eldest daughter.

Until that moment I believed beauty to exist only in flowers. But this girl was more exquisite than any flower. Her shape was finer, her colouring more delicate, her movements more graceful. Kindness, wisdom and passion met in eyes as darkly mysterious as the mountain lakes beside which she had grown up.

Transfixed, I smiled at her across the glowing ashes. When she smiled back, my heart jumped. I was trapped as tight as any snared animal. From that moment forward she was the centre of my universe, all I thought of when awake and all I dreamed of when sleeping.

I had to make Laughing Water my wife.

Among the Indian peoples a young man has to prove himself to a girl's father before he may ask her hand in marriage. I began straight away the next morning when a young brave challenged me to a shooting match. I won, finally blasting out the crown of his hat when it was thrown into the air. Laughing Water had watched the contest from afar, and after my victory I waved to her. She returned my greeting with a laugh more lovely than the song of the skylark.

Next, I explained to Chief Cockqua how far I was going to travel as part of my work. It was through dangerous territory, too, where bears and unfriendly Indians might attack at any moment.

The chief was impressed. 'Grass Man,' he observed, calling me by my tribal name, 'if you return alive, you will have shown yourself as strong as any of my people.'

It was just what I wanted to hear. 'I will come back alive, Great Chief,' I replied, 'and I will make the journey in ninety days.'

'That cannot be done, Grass Man!' The response only strengthened my resolve. If I could achieve the impossible, in three months Laughing Water would surely be mine.

I did it. I covered over 1,100 miles of uncharted territory in eighty-eight days, collecting samples of cones and seeds as I went. It was not easy, mind you. In a single day – the worst of my entire expedition – I faced death on no less than four separate occasions.

Rising early, I had set out to climb a rocky crag on whose summit I had been told grew a rare type of lichen. The way up was easy and a couple of hours after sunrise I had the lichen safely in my bag and was gazing in wonder over an unspoilt wilderness of wild peaks and dense evergreen forest.

The sight was so exhilarating that I began my descent with a spring in my step – too much spring, it turned out. After a few lively paces I lost my footing and began to roll down the slope. My fall disturbed the rocks and stones on either side of me, so that within a few seconds I was part of a small landslide.

God preserve me, I prayed, for I am surely going to die.

I was saved by a large boulder projecting from the mountainside. Being heavier than the stones with which I was travelling, as we hurtled over it I fell into its shadow while lighter objects bounced on towards the forest. For a full ten minutes I lay panting behind the rock, slowly regaining my composure. Fortunately, although I had received some nasty cuts and bruises, none of my bones were broken and the bag of samples strapped to my back was undamaged.

Proceeding on my journey with greater caution, I saw to my dismay that the landslide had disturbed some of the local wildlife – to be precise, a vast grizzly bear. The beast was snuffling about at the edge of the forest ahead of me. He was clearly angry at having been bombarded with falling rocks and was looking for someone to blame.

We saw each other at the same time. The grizzly paused, wondering what to make of the battered oddity clattering towards it. I, on the other hand, did not pause. I ran to my left, making for the river in the valley below. Soon I was in the forest, darting as quickly as I could over the soft carpet of pine needles. The crashing noise behind me made it quite clear that the bear had decided I was responsible for its pelting and wanted revenge.

The river was wider and deeper than I had anticipated. It was also icy cold. My choice was stark: almost certain death in the teeth and razor claws of the grizzly, or an almost equally certain death in the freezing current before me. I chose the water.

Holding my bag high above my head, I walked into the stream. The cold took my breath away. I waded out until the water was up to my chin, and looked back. My pursuer had wisely decided not to follow and was pacing up and down the bank waiting for my return.

There was no going back. Taking a deep breath, I launched myself into the stream. Immediately the current took hold and carried me rapidly away from the bear. Glad to be out of that particular danger but gasping for breath and struggling to hold my bag clear of the torrent, I kicked and pulled with my free arm until my feet eventually touched firm bottom on the opposite bank.

Shaking like a steam engine, I hauled myself to the shore. With my clothes saturated, my hands numb, and my brain almost at a standstill, I staggered out of the water and gazed blearily about me. Although I did not realize it until that moment, my antics had been closely observed by a party of Indian braves that had now gathered on the bank to inspect me more closely. I knew their tribe well – it was not friendly towards white men.

There was no point in fighting. I had no gun and my knife was in my bag, while the Indians carried both bows and muskets. My slow and frozen brain could come up with only one idea – bluff.

'I am the Great Man of the River!' I cried in the native tongue, raising myself to my full height. The Indians smiled.

'Each day I come from the waters to bring . . .

cr . . . goodness and life to the land.' I have never been much of an actor, and this performance was undoubtedly the feeblest of my life.

The Indians thought so too. First one, then the whole band burst into hoots of laughter. When they had regained their composure, they decided that I was a mad fool who posed no danger to them, and so went on their way.

That day as every day, the image of Laughing Water was my strength and inspiration. Its loveliness drove from my mind any possibility of failure. Her face floated before me as I walked, while at night it danced in the starry sky above. A thousand times I imagined holding her dear hand in mine. I dreamed of taking her with me back to Scotland and walking proudly through the streets of Edinburgh with her on my arm. Had the journey been twice as long, for her love I would have endured it.

Two weeks after setting out I suffered a nasty fall which broke my spectacles and badly damaged my left arm. I lost my hat, too, and replaced it with a battered straw affair bought from a passing Indian. On the hills a biting wind drove gritty dust into my eyes. They became so red and swollen that, unless

I screwed them up tight, I could hardly see. Two of my three shirts fell apart completely. By the end of my pilgrimage the third was little more than tatters. My trousers were in no better condition, barely covering my scratched and bleeding legs. The destruction of my wardrobe was completed by the wearing out of my shoes, obliging me to go barefoot.

The lean and bearded man with a sack of samples on his back who staggered from the woods by Cockqua's village was quite unlike the sprightly young fellow who had marched out so proudly less than three months before. I did not care – I had triumphed! What was more, as if Fate herself was smiling on us, there was my angel coming down the path towards me.

She was even lovelier than I remembered her!

I stopped and waited for her to draw near. When she was no more than two paces away, she glanced up into my face, held my look for a second, and then modestly lowered her gaze. Her eyes had given no flash of welcome, nor had even a hint of a smile come to her lips.

Laughing Water had not recognized me.

Without lifting her head again, she walked quickly by and disappeared into the trees. I was too stunned to speak. I knew that all my actions had been in vain. With stumbling steps I crossed the village and made my way down to the European settlement beyond.

TOUGH ENOUGH?

Frank Kingdon Ward

T he son of a Cambridge professor of botany, Frank Kingdon Ward (1885–1958) was an obsessive explorer and botanist. Undaunted by danger, during the course of his extraordinary life he made twenty-two remarkable overseas expeditions to collect and catalogue seeds and specimens from the wild. His tireless efforts led to over one hundred species of rhododendron being introduced to the wider world. Nevertheless, not all his trips were successful . . .

The expedition started badly and got worse.

From Hpimaw, Frank Kingdon Ward and his party of Burmese helpers had set out for the mountains. A glance at the map had suggested that all they had to do was follow the ridge north, then cut across west to the Assam region of north-east India.

Maps and reality, however, rarely correspond. To begin with it rained all day and all night. Not a nice gentle shower, but bullet-hard, sluicing, tropical rain. After just one day's travel all their possessions were soaked through: clothes, tents, bedding, bags, papers, seed boxes. Within a week everything that could go mouldy did so. Frank even found fungus sprouting on his underpants.

As on his previous trips, twenty-nine-year-old Frank was travelling for Arthur Bulley of Bees Seeds. Bulley had a very appropriate name, Frank thought, as he sloshed through the mud of the lower slopes. He had been delighted with the results of Frank's previous expedition. He had even agreed that one beautiful new species of rhododendron should be given the Latin name *Wardii* in honour of its discoverer.

But that was 1913. His thirst for new species unquenched, Bulley had asked Frank to set out again the following year. 'Try Burma, young man,' he had suggested enthusiastically. 'Somewhere remote and mountainous. Bound to find some splendid undiscovered flora there.'

So it was that the fateful summer of 1914, only weeks before the outbreak of world war, found Frank slithering through the mud of north-east Burma in search of botanical specimens to delight the scientific curiosity and gardens of his generous but demanding patrons.

Anyone who has experienced tropical rain knows that it is usually accompanied by something even more unpleasant. Leeches.

These creatures fell onto Frank from overhanging branches, fastened their jaws upon him from long grass, and squirmed into him while he lay sleeping. No matter what he did, the fat black bloodsuckers always found a way through his clothing and onto his skin. They seemed to like fair skin, too, for the vile worms targeted his travelling companions far less than himself.

After a couple of hours' walk through dense

vegetation, Frank would stop for a leech inspection. There were always three or four attached to his neck, swaying gently and swelling as they gorged themselves on his blood. The rest were harder to find. Some crept under his shirt, others snaked deep beneath his trousers.

Removing them was not a pleasant task. Frank knew they should not be pulled off. When that happened, they left their jaws embedded in the skin. The wounds often developed into dripping sores. Instead, each leech was supposed to be driven off by pouring salt on it or touching it with a burning cigarette.

Frank could not be bothered with such a tedious process. He just grabbed the leeches between his fingers and pulled, leaving behind a bleeding hole. After ten days of travel his body was a mass of septic sores.

It took more than leeches to deter Frank Kingdon Ward. Ignoring his wounds and the slight fever that was now coming upon him, he led his team onward and upward.

One night a terrible storm broke over their camp. Frank was woken by a frightening screeching and tearing. The next moment, a branch as thick as a pillar-box crashed on top of his tent, almost pinning him to the ground. Grabbing a machete, the brave botanist hacked his way through the tangle of canvas, rope and twisted foliage. When he had finally cut himself free, he looked back and saw that a huge tree had blown down onto his tent. It was a miracle that he had survived.

As if to test his luck, the same thing happened again shortly afterwards. This time he was sleeping in a village hut. The falling tree smashed it completely and he had to escape through a hole in what was left of the roof. Disasters come in threes, thought Frank. Leeches and two falling trees make my quota. He looked forward to things getting easier from then on.

If anything, they got worse.

They were now high in the mountains of north-east Burma. Frank found some delightful and unusual species of flower and safely collected their seeds. One morning, though, reaching over a precipice for a type of poppy he had not seen before, he lost his footing. Arms flailing, he began to slide into the gulf. As he fell, he caught a glimpse of the blue river hundreds of feet below him. This is it, he thought, the last journey of Frank Kingdon Ward.

Flying by a small tree growing out of the rock face, Frank made a wild grab at one of its branches. His hand closed over the rough bark. The branch bent, cracked – but did not break. Slowly and carefully, he his way to the base of the tree where he found a foothold. For a minute or so he clung there, panting. Unable to climb any higher, he called for help. At first his Burmese companions could not work out where the noise was coming from. When they eventually realized, they lowered a rope and hauled him up to safety.

Back on the summit, Frank mused on his narrow escape. I've risked my life for the local flora, he thought as he straightened his clothes, so perhaps it's only right they should help me out now and again. He peered back over the precipice. 'Thank you, tree!' he called. 'I'd do the same for you if I could.'

One dark night three weeks later, as Frank was checking that all was well in the camp, he stumbled and rolled down a stony slope. His fall was broken by a low ledge. Thinking nothing of the incident, he picked himself up and went back to his tent. In

the morning, out of curiosity, he returned to the spot. Behind the ledge the ground fell away thousands of feet into the valley below. He'd narrowly missed death yet again!

By this time Frank was in poor shape. He was racked with malaria and very thin. His sores showed little sign of healing. The sensible thing would have been to make for the nearest town straight away. But Frank was not a man to take the easy path. There were a couple of mountains he wished to climb first.

Eventually, totally exhausted and shaking with fever, Frank reached Fort Konglu, a far-flung military outpost of the British Empire. The commanding officer welcomed him warmly. He was fed, given a clean bed and a doctor dressed his wounds. Within hours of his arrival he was known around the camp as the 'dotty botanist'.

The following evening, already feeling much better, Frank strolled across to the officers' mess. Inside he found a couple of men enjoying a gin and lime.

'I say,' remarked the taller of the two as Frank entered, 'if it isn't the seed hunter! Come in, old boy! I'm Henry Kircauldie. Want a drink?'

As the lieutenant was ordering him a glass of cold beer, Frank turned to the second man. 'Frank Kingdon Ward,' he said, stretching out his hand.

The soldier grasped it. 'Nice to meet you, Ward. I'm Childers, George Childers. By the way, have you heard the news that came though this morning?'

Frank shook his head. 'I haven't heard any news from back home since I left Hpimaw months ago.'

'My word!' exclaimed Childers. 'Well, I'm afraid you're in for a bit of shock. It's war, you know.'

'War? Oh dear! You mean a civil war in China? Or is it in Ireland? I know things were pretty dicey there when I left.'

'China? Ireland?' exclaimed Kircauldie, handing Frank his beer. 'Heavens, man! Much more important than that! The British and French Empires are head to head with the Germans and the Austrians. It's a big show, I can tell you.'

Frank's beer remained untasted in his hand. 'Well, if that's the case, I think I'd better get back to civilization as quickly as possible and join the army.'

Kircauldie raised an eyebrow and glanced across at Childers. 'Of course, Ward. But this is real war, you know. I don't want to sound rude or anything, but do you reckon you're up to it? Will a botanist chappie like you be tough enough, eh?'

A thin smile came to Frank's lips. 'Tough enough, Kircauldie?' he said quietly. 'Why, yes. As it happens, I think I probably am tough enough.'

Zheng He

*I*n the early fifteenth century, Admiral Zheng He commanded the enormous Chinese Treasure Fleet. Emperor Zhu Di sent the fleet on several voyages as far as Arabia and Africa to show his power to the 'barbarians' of other lands. After each trip Zheng He unloaded gifts of tribute that included many species of tree and plant previously unknown in China. Madam Wang, the emperor's ageing chief mistress and a close friend of Zheng He, took a particular interest in the progress of the Treasure Fleet . . .

96

There are two men in my life. One needs little introduction. He is my master, the Ming Emperor of the Dragon Throne. His name is Zhu Di, the Bringer of Lasting Joy. My children are his, my heart is his, my body is his. I am his lady, Madam Wang, and he is my lord.

I pray that Zhu Di and I will be as one until the day I die. Yet the hearts of men – even of emperors – change like the moon, so I cannot be sure. This is why I am so delighted at the return of Zheng He and his Treasure Fleet from its latest voyage, for they have brought me what I desire more than anything else in the world.

Admiral Zheng He, as you may have guessed, is the other man in my life. To be accurate, 'man' is not quite correct. Zheng He is in fact a eunuch, having been castrated at the age of fourteen. Now you understand that there is nothing unwholesome in the relationship between myself and my dear friend Zheng He. We are like brother and sister. It is wise not to say as much in public, though. Even for eunuchs, close friendships with the emperor's ladies are not welcomed. My lord and master Zhu Di is a fiercely jealous man.

*

Zheng He and Zhu Di met many years ago. It was during the campaign fought by the first Ming dynasty emperor against the rebellious Mongol people of Yunnan. They refused to accept the rule of the Ming and proclaimed one of their own people emperor in his place. Zhu Di, then a mere prince, went with a great army to crush them and destroy their pretend emperor. He killed many thousands, sparing neither men, women nor children in his fury.

No, that is not quite right. He did spare one. It was a ten-year-old lad he found wandering by the wayside. 'Boy, where is your pretend emperor?' demanded the prince as he rode by.

The boy thought for a moment before replying, 'He leaped into a pond.'

The reply so infuriated Zhu Di's attendants that they were all for cutting off the child's head there and then. But the prince bade them put up their swords. 'This boy is clever,' he observed. 'Only a fool destroys what one day might be of use to him. Bring him with us and raise him in my household.'

So began the relationship between my lord and his

loyal servant Zheng He. At around that time the prince welcomed me into his palace, so the boy and I grew up together. I saw him mature into a tall and strong man, with a high brow and sharp eyes. The prince had been right about his intelligence. Zheng He devoured books as most men devour rice, and stored all he read in a brain as capacious as a barn. Unusually for men of learning, he was practical too.

Zheng He's practicality showed itself when his master – and I must be careful how I express this – fulfilled the wish of heaven. In other words, after several long wars he seized China's Dragon Throne from his brother. Zheng's skill as a general played a big part in Zhu Di's triumph, and he was rewarded with many honours.

All this time my friendship with Zheng He was blossoming. We talked together for hours. I learned from him and, I believe, he learned from me. 'You know, Madam Wang,' he said to me one day, 'women do not see the world the way men do. Some say they understand less than men. Talking to you, I do not think it so. Indeed, sometimes I think they understand more. Not through learning, for they are not educated like men, but through insight. You can see into men's souls – that is a great gift which I do not possess.'

I was flattered. It is not often that men compliment women in this manner, yet I believe it to be true. It is part of the secret of our power – as you shall shortly see.

No sooner had my lord Zhu Di ascended the Dragon Throne than he began the greatest project ever undertaken in this noble land of ours. He is an ambitious and proud man. Now he had China in his grasp, he wanted more. All the barbarian peoples of the known world, he declared, should recognize him as their king.

To this end he ordered a multitude of ships to be built. Among their number were vessels larger and more magnificent than any ever seen in the world before. Four of them – which he called the 'turrets of his ocean castle' – were more than four hundred feet long with no less than nine masts bearing sails that filled the sky like billowing clouds. There was nothing such ships could not carry: men by the thousand, horses, weapons, food and all kinds of merchandise. To them the angriest waves raised by the dragons of the deep were but ripples. I wept with wonder when I saw them in Nanjing harbour for the first time.

After three years of work the mighty Treasure Fleet was ready. Riding at anchor were 317 noble vessels carrying 28,000 loyal subjects of our majestic emperor. All they lacked was a commander.

Many men had been suggested for the post, most of them young and energetic. I knew they were not suitable. I wanted only one man to be admiral of the Treasure Fleet. I wanted him because he was my friend and because I was beginning to realize that I needed his help if I were to remain the emperor's favourite lady.

One evening, as my lord lay resting, I came to him. I stroked his noble cheek and, seeking to turn the conversation along the path I desired, I asked him about his great Treasure Fleet. A furrow came upon his brow.

'You know, my cherry, I cannot decide who should be its admiral. Some say our faithful servant Zheng He would be the man. Yet he is old and might not survive the rigours of the sea.'

At this I placed my arms about my lord's neck and said quietly, 'Old, master? He has seen but thirty-five summers. He is still young in heart and mind, just as you are, who have seen more.'

A slight smile flickered over the emperor's lips. I took his hand and continued, 'Like ginger and dates and Zhu Di, some things get better with age. Do you not recall the proverb, "An old horse knows the way"?'

The emperor's smile broadened. 'Look at Zheng He's face,' I went on. 'It's rough like an orange, showing his experience and toughness. His eyes are set quite close together, indicating firmness of purpose. Words flow from his mouth like the waters of the sea. His eyes sparkle—'

'Enough!' my lord commanded. 'You will make me think you love him if you continue like that. Yet I am convinced by what you say. Zheng He shall command my Treasure Fleet.'

I could scarcely contain my joy.

The emperor rose to his feet and began walking towards the door. After four or five strides he stopped and turned back towards me. 'Remember this, Madam Wang, I am making this appointment on your advice. If your friend Zheng He fails me, you will have failed me too.'

Zheng He failed neither the emperor nor myself. Indeed, his successes far exceeded expectation.

Returning from his first expedition, he was, again at my suggestion, ordered to prepare for another, then another and another. He has now led five voyages of the Treasure Fleet and it is rumoured that still my lord is not satisfied. Next year, they say, my friend will set out on a sixth voyage. I hope this is not true, for I miss his wise company when he is away and, as you shall hear, he has already fulfilled the task I set him.

The Treasure Fleet has visited every half-civilized country under the heavens and wrung submission from every one of their kings and princes. The only peoples Zheng He does not know well are the inhabitants of those distant, damp and grey lands that lie beyond Egypt. We have heard stories of the primitive natives who dwell there – barbaric and dirty tribes – but do not consider them worth a visit.

Amazingly, the ambassadors of the Dragon Throne have occasionally met with resistance. Zheng He has told me many stories of how he overcame all who refused to recognize his master. The pirates of the narrow seas were perhaps his toughest adversaries, although the warriors of Sri Lanka put up a stiff fight. One foe he never vanquished. These

were the were-tigers of Malaya, black-striped beasts
that live in huts thatched with women's hair. Our
sailors refused to approach them and left those
cursed shores as quickly as they could.

I am no fighter, and tales of blood and beasts are
not what I really like to hear. I prefer it when my
friend tells of his more light-hearted adventures. He
can be very funny when he sets his mind to it. Unlike
most soldiers, his wit is sharp and dry. His most
amusing tales are of Siam, where the men are ruled
by the women. Would I had been born in such a
place! Zheng He assures me that it is the height of
fashion for Siamese men to wear in their groin tiny
round bells that tinkle as they walk. How peculiar!
I wonder if it is really so?

The tribute with which my friend returned was
more than our storehouses could hold. I will begin
with the animals and birds, for they interest me
least. There were tigers and lions and elephants by
the score. Even more numerous were the girls from
Korea for the adornment of His Majesty's household.
I'm told there were one hundred of them. I know
I should have been jealous, but I was not. None of
them were very pretty. Besides, soon I will no longer
fear the blossom of youth.

The greatest fuss was made over a mythical long-necked and long-legged creature known as a qilin. His Majesty was very proud of it. He said it was the first time one of these animals had ever been seen outside the pages of a book. Actually, Zheng He says it is not a qilin at all but something called a giraffe. They are, he tells me, as common as horses in Africa. This is a secret, however. If Zhu Di ever learned the truth he would probably have us both beheaded.

Enough of these grim thoughts! I wander from the purpose of my story. What you wish to know is why I was so eager for Zheng He to command the Treasure Fleet, and what it is that I was so eager for him to bring back. Listen!

On his last voyage my friend took a special guest with him, Dr Kuang Yu. Dr Yu is a specialist in medicinal herbs and spices, and he travelled with Zheng He at my personal request. Let me explain.

Each time the Admiral returned, the Treasure Fleet was laden with every spice you can imagine, including precious nutmeg and scented cloves. There were sweet smelling tree resins, too, and special woods like ebony and aloe. From Africa came plants, shrubs and even entire trees. The latter were carefully dug up so that the soil around their roots was not disturbed. Shipped back to China, they now beautify the palaces and gardens of the Dragon Emperor.

All these things were very wonderful, but they were not what I was hoping for. I wanted something special, magical even. As you probably realize by now, I am no longer a young woman. My charms fade with each passing season. In the morning my skin is dry and cracked like summer fields, and grey steals into my hair. As this happens, so my hold over Zhu Di is weakened.

That is why Zheng He took Dr Yu with him on his last voyage. The doctor had orders to seek out the plant that gives eternal life. He took many baskets, supplied by me, and returned with them all full of medicinal herbs and plants. Some we have seen before but many are new to our land. In one of them my hope lies.

On an African shore, guided by Zheng He, Dr Yu traded the finest silken cloth with an elderly Arab merchant. In return he was given just a few leaves of a small plant that grows on the slopes of a sacred mountain they call Kilimanjaro. Specially prepared, the juice of this plant will bring eternal life to all who drink it.

Dr Yu will begin his treatment on me tomorrow. Under his careful guidance my youth will return and I will be the Emperor's favourite lady for ever!

Meriwether Lewis

*T*he naturalist Meriwether Lewis (1774–1809) and the geographer William Clark (1770–1838) led the first scientific expedition to cross North America. Leaving the eastern states in 1803, the party of American pioneers reached the Pacific Ocean via the Ohio, Mississippi, Missouri and Colombia Rivers. Where possible, they travelled by boat. For long stretches of the remarkable eight thousand mile journey, though, they struggled along on foot and horseback. By the time of their return *in 1806, they had gathered an immense amount of information on the geography, flora and fauna of the largely unexplored North American continent. Clark, the more balanced and diplomatic of the two men, went on to work on relations between white settlers and native Indians. Lewis was of a less stable character . . .*

I met the great Mr Meriwether Lewis shortly before he died. I call him 'great' because of what he and Mr William Clark did – crossing the American continent and all that. I heard a man in St Louis say the maps Mr Clark made of this great land of ours will be used for one hundred years at least. The boxes of plant specimens and such like gathered up by Mr Lewis filled every ground floor room of the Grand Hotel – excepting the bathrooms – and that's a mighty lot of boxes.

When I met Mr Lewis you wouldn't have called him great. No sir! He was thin as a snake, scruffy and drinking whiskey straight from the bottle all day long. Great shame when the booze gets hold of a man like that.

I was travelling down the Mississippi on a barge, heading for New Orleans where I had some business to attend to. Lewis was on the same boat. He was governor of Louisiana at the time, so maybe he too was on some kind of business. I don't know.

We got talking, like men do. I told him who I was and after a bit of evasion he did the same. He must have seen the surprise in my face, because straight away he said, 'I know what you're thinking, Mr Singleton. I can read you like a Bible. You're right, too. I have become rather fond of my fiery friend here.' He slapped the side of his coat and I could hear the sound of bottles clinking inside.

I ignored his remark and begged him to tell me something of his adventures. He gave me a weary look, like he was tired of storytelling. His face changed, though, when I put my next question. 'Mr Lewis,' I said, 'on your crossing, did you have any trouble with bears?'

'Bears, Mr Singleton?' Lewis exclaimed. 'Why, I nearly met my end in the claws of a grizzly.'

'Tell me about it,' I replied, quick as a flash to keep his mind from wandering.

'I sure will, Singleton. Just listen.'

So, leaning against the rail and gazing out over the cotton fields, no less a person than Mr Meriwether Lewis himself told me this tale.

*

The party knew what they were looking for. It was marked on their charts as 'Great Lake River' and it flowed westwards from the Rocky Mountains to the sea. Once they were on it, Lewis and Clark knew all they had to do was build themselves some rafts, load up all the specimens that Lewis had collected and float into history.

Trouble was, this Great Lake River wasn't easy to find. The Indians said it was near another river called the Medicine. So one day, when Lewis learned that the Medicine was not too far off, he reckoned he'd go and take a look for himself. He shouldered a gun with which to shoot himself a buffalo for his supper and headed down towards the cottonwoods that grew along the river valley.

After a hike of several hours, during which he plucked and stowed away some dainty looking flowers he didn't know the name of, Lewis chose a tidy spot for a camp and selected himself a handsome buffalo from a small herd that was grazing nearby. He took aim and his shot hit the beast in the chest. With blood pouring out of its mouth and nose, it sank slowly down and died. Now, as he was going over to make sure it was dead, Lewis heard a noise that was somewhere between a pounding and a shuffle.

He looked up and saw he wasn't alone. A great grizzly bear was lumbering through the grass towards him. Lewis didn't hang around to see whether it was him or the buffalo meat the animal wanted. Just as well. It was soon pretty obvious what the bear was after. Grizzlies don't take too kindly to folk that come nosing round their territory and disturbing the wildlife with their guns.

If Lewis had not just shot the buffalo, he might have been able to use his bullet on the bear. As it was, he had no time to reload. First, he thought he'd get into the tree he'd chosen to camp under, but a quick look told him that plan wasn't going to work. The grizzly would be on him before he could climb beyond the reach of those clasp-knife claws.

Plan two was to head for the river. Lewis sprinted till he thought his lungs would burst open like a busted barrel. He made it to the bank and fell the last few feet into the water. His pursuer was more canny. It paused at the top and came down the bank carefully, keeping its beady bear eyes on Lewis all the while to make sure he didn't make a bolt for it.

The explorer waded into the stream until the water came up above his waist. If he went any further, he could lose his footing and be swept away to certain death. Meanwhile, the bear was easing itself into the river like a lady into her bath.

Lewis remembered someone once telling him that grizzlies with wet feet were less fierce than those on dry land. Well, it was not the sort of information you check out just for fun, so Lewis didn't know whether it was true or not. Stuck there in the river, though, he reckoned it was time to find out.

He chose to start with eye contact, staring hard into the eyes of the bear. The creature didn't even notice. Right, let's try movement, Lewis thought. He waved his spiked stick over his head like some kind of spear. The beast ignored that too and advanced closer still. By this time Lewis was growing desperate. All he had left to try was noise. Continuing to stare and wave, he took up hollering at the top of his voice like a demented preacher.

The bear stopped. It gave Lewis a strange look. It'd never met an animal like this before and didn't know what to make of it. Flapping his arms and shouting, the explorer took a step towards the grizzly. He was so close he could almost feel the warmth of its breath. The animal blinked and shook its head. Lewis took another step. This confused the bear and it swatted the air a couple of times with its paws. Then it turned, waded back to the shore, and disappeared into the trees.

Lewis let out a whoop of triumph. Smiling like his face would split, he returned to the shore. After reloading his gun, he explored the river a bit more before returning to base. No, he told Clark, he didn't reckon the Medicine River would lead them to the Pacific Ocean. But all the same, he was mighty glad it was there.

Christopher Columbus

When Christopher Columbus led his first Spanish expedition westwards across the Atlantic in 1492, he was trying to reach Asia. He was not aware of the existence of the Americas. To the day he died he believed that gold-rich Japan lay only a short distance beyond the unspoilt islands – which we know as the Bahamas and the West Indies – that he discovered. Although he is famous as the first European since Viking times to reach the Americas, rather than as a plant hunter, his *expeditions revealed hundreds of species of flora previously unknown to the rest of the world.*

My name is Juan Arias. No, you have not heard of me. I am not famous. But I have served with Captain Columbus and other renowned sailors who performed deeds that my country is proud of.

I myself am not proud of them. That is why I am dictating this to Father Quintero, the honest priest who has looked after me since I was a child. Only he believes me when I swear that I have seen something no human being should ever see.

The plague carried my parents and my brothers and sisters off to heaven when I was six years old. Unwilling to see me die of starvation, Father Quintero took me into his household where I was looked after by Doña Concepcion, his housekeeper.

What a storyteller she was! Each afternoon, while the reverend father was taking his siesta, she sat me beside her on the rough kitchen bench and recounted a tale from the Bible, spicing each one with details of her own imagining. Solomon, she insisted, had one brown eye and one green one because he was born in May when the grass was beginning to wither in the summer heat. For a long time the adventures of Moses in Egypt were my favourites, but that was because she had saved the best until last.

Bible stories normally begin with the Book of Genesis and the making of the world. Doña Concepcion saw things differently. First, she said, it was necessary to learn of people's wickedness. Only then could I understand why it had come about. It was not until my ninth year, therefore, that I heard her version of the ghastly tale of what had happened to Adam and Eve in the Garden of Eden.

I sat petrified as she painted in words an unforgettable picture of the devil transforming himself into a long, languid snake. The creature then lurked in the garden, slowly coiling and uncoiling around the trunk of the Tree of Knowledge. In my mind's eye I saw the rosy apple, the fruit that God had forbidden Adam and Eve to eat. I could almost taste its sweetness. And how I felt for Eve when she realized that one bite had doomed all mankind to an eternity of sin!

From a young age I had wanted to become a priest, like Father Quintero. He thought it was a good idea and devoted many hours to helping me with my studies. On my twelfth birthday, however, he suggested that to be a good priest I needed first to see the world, to learn about the people whom I wished to serve. He introduced me to a sea captain friend of his, Vincente Pinzon. Captain Pinzon agreed to give me the position of cabin boy on his ship the *Nina*.

So it was that I found myself on that famous fleet which Captain Christopher Columbus led across the vast and empty ocean to the Indies. I shared the men's fear when no land was sighted for days and days, and I shared their delight when an island appeared like a mirage on the horizon. Yet that was when I felt the first pangs of the shame that now rules my life.

The sailors competed with each other to be the first to see land. They did so not because it would confirm God's handiwork in making a world as round and perfect as a hazelnut. Neither did they do so for honour or glory. They looked for one thing only – gold. The king and queen had offered several pieces to he who first caught sight of the Indies.

*

We landed first on an island that Columbus called San Salvador. To me Eden would have been a more fitting name. A beach of silver sand sloped gently up to trees of such bright green that I believed them to have been newly painted. The fruits that hung there were larger and more delicious than any found in Spain. Parrots coloured like the glass of a church window flashed across the clear blue sky. The air was warm and filled with birdsong. Yes, it was paradise indeed.

Soon the island's inhabitants were flocking to greet us. Beautiful men and women they were, entirely naked. With smiles and signs of worship they fell at our feet and pressed simple gifts on us. These gentle, kind people reminded me of something, but at the time I could not recollect what it was.

Captain Pinzon agreed that the island was a good place and its people handsome, yet his mind was already elsewhere. He and Columbus pointed at the rings of gold that the natives wore in their ears and demanded to know from whence the metal came. When hands indicated a land to the south, we boarded our ships and continued our journey. At the command of our leader seven natives were seized and brought on board as gifts for the king and queen back in Spain. That night I was awakened by their crying.

So we sailed to another island and yet another. Each was equally beautiful and the inhabitants as friendly and simple as those of San Salvador. Columbus was not satisfied, though. Paradise was not enough for him. He wanted gold.

By the time we reached an island that Columbus named Fernandina in honour of our king, my spirit was deeply troubled. I felt in my bones that something was wrong with our whole expedition, yet I could not put my finger on it. I wished to be alone with my thoughts and, leaving the rest of the crew on the beach, I wandered inland.

As before, I delighted in the richness and beauty of the plants and trees that grew in such profusion. With the sweet scent of a thousand delicate flowers delighting my nostrils, I was in the very Garden of Eden itself! After a while, feeling hungry, I plucked a fruit whose name I did not know and ate it. As I proceeded, the forest began to turn hazy before my eyes. The vegetation seemed to be swaying, as if to music.

Confused, in a trance-like state, I stared at the

writhing branches of a low tree that rose up before me. The moving limbs were as thick as a man's arm and a dazzling yellow in colour. As I gazed, horrified, one branch took on a new form and appeared to slide towards me.

With a cry of terror, I leaped backwards. The thing was not a branch at all. It was a snake – a great golden serpent with a flickering black tongue and eyes like emeralds! It was just like the devil-snake in Doña Concepcion's stories, the beastly form that the Evil One had taken.

As I watched, transfixed, it raised its head and opened its mouth as if to laugh at me. But the noise that it uttered was not a merry one. It was a long, vile hiss that came to my ear as human speech: 'The success of Satan is assured.'

At that I turned and ran screaming through the forest towards the shore. When I arrived, pale and panting, my fellow sailors asked me what had happened. Why did I look so scared?

'Serpent!' I gasped. 'I have seen a terrible serpent.'

The men laughed and said there were no snakes on these islands. I was mocked about the incident for the rest of the voyage. When they said the sea air had made me mad, I shouted at them and called them fools and liars. I was delivered back to Father Quintero in chains.

Since my experience in the Indies I have thought of little else. I do not believe I was in a trance or dreaming – the vision was too real for that. No, I am convinced that the confession I am about to make is the true interpretation of what happened:

Almighty God led us safely across the Atlantic Ocean. On the other side he showed us Paradise. Like Adam and Eve before us, we rejected his gift and went in search of gold. That is why the snake was there – the golden serpent was Satan himself rejoicing at our folly. In the forest of Fernandina, Eden on Earth, I came face to face with the Devil.

Deep in a giant crater in Cornwall are the two biggest greenhouses in the world – the famous Biomes of the Eden Project, where you can enter a lush tropical rainforest or the dry, scented lands of the Mediterranean.

They were created to show people just how much we depend on plants to feed and clothe us. You can see for yourself the trees and fruits and flowers that become chocolate, baked beans, rubber tyres, cotton T-shirts, paper for books and much more.

You can discover plants at Eden through music, art and storytelling – and through Eden Project books too!

www.edenproject.com

EDEN PROJECT BOOKS

Grow Your Own Sweet Peas
Grow Your Own Nasturtiums

Poems from Eden
Annamaria Murphy

Adam and Eve and the Garden of Eden
Jane Ray

The World Came to My Place Today
Jo Readman and Ley Honor Roberts

My Eden Activity Book
Ley Honor Roberts

Revenge of the Green Planet
Astounding Facts About Plants

A Child's Guide to Wild Flowers
Charlotte Voake

My Flower, Your Flower
Melanie Walsh

REVENGE OF THE GREEN PLANET
Astounding Facts About Plants

Believe it or not . . .

Some plants grow at a rate of more than
half a metre a day.

Others look like green lavatory bowls
full of digesting fluid.

One particular bush has been growing
continuously for 40,000 years.

BE WARNED . . . the Green Things are
taking over the planet. They are already the
dominant life form on Earth, making up 99%
of all living things, so you'd better start
showing a bit of respect!

This book contains hundreds of fascinating
facts to keep you informed, impress your
friends and amuse your family.

Eden Project Books
1 903 91905 3

THE SHORT AND BLOODY HISTORY OF PIRATES
John Farman

All aboard, landlubbers!

Have you ever wondered why pirates wore gold earrings, or where the saying 'sick as a parrot' came from? And do you know who the cruellest pirate in history was?

John Farman's got all the answers, so come aboard for his short and bloody history of the day-to-day life of pirates!

Red Fox
0 099 40709 4

THE SHORT AND BLOODY
HISTORY OF KNIGHTS
John Farman

Fancy a joust?

Have you ever wondered how knights
managed to walk, let alone fight, covered
from head to foot in metal? And have you
heard about the knights who became addicted
to jousting? Or the one that was rescued by a
monkey? It's all in John Farman's brilliant
book. So arm yourself for a fact attack!

Red Fox
0 099 40712 2

THE SHORT AND BLOODY
HISTORY OF HIGHWAYMEN
John Farman

Stand and deliver!

Have you ever wondered what highwaymen
did during the day? And do you know who
the most devious highwayman was, or which
roads used to be the most dangerous in
Britain? John Farman's ready to stand and
deliver all the answers, so take a closer look at
this short and bloody history of highwaymen!

Red Fox
0 099 45958 2

KINGS AND QUEENS
Tony Robinson

Kings and Queens have always provided
their subjects with a great deal to talk about.
But how much do we really know about
them? For instance, who became King
when he was only nine months old? Which
king died on the toilet? And who is England's
longest reigning monarch? Tony Robinson
provides the answers to these questions
and many more...

Red Fox
0 099 41748 0

HOW ANGEL PETERSON GOT HIS NAME
Gary Paulsen

Just remember – DON'T TRY THIS AT HOME!

Can you imagine wanting to try any of
these insane stunts?

- Shooting over a waterfall in a barrel!
- Wrestling a bear at a carnival!
- Hitching behind a car on a home-made skateboard!
- Taking to the skies under a giant kite!
- Skiing along behind a racing car!
- Jumping to the ground on a home-made
bungee cord!

It's hard to believe, but these crazy exploits are
Gary, Orvis and Carl's idea of fun! These hilarious
tales of the original extreme sports are totally
unbelievable, jaw-droppingly dangerous and
completely unputdownable!

From the award-winning and best-selling author
of Hatchet and Dogsong, Gary Paulsen.

Corgi Books
0 552 54807 3

THE VERY BLOODY HISTORY
OF LONDON
John Farman

'When a man is tired of London, he is tired of life . . .' Samuel Johnson

One of the world's most famous cities is sized up by John Farman. London's history is brought to life by powerful storytelling, fact-packed pages and wildly funny interpretations of some of the city's well-known and less well-known landmarks.

Red Fox
0 099 40412 5